SELF ESTEEM WORKBOOK FOR CHRISTIAN WOMEN

By: Wellness for Women

ANXIETY
Journal & Workbook

This Book Belongs To

Name:

Phone:

Email:

Introduction

Anxiety can be debilitating. Instead of being able to enjoy a moment and be in the present, self-criticism and anxiety can create warped thinking where you are is constantly beating yourself up.

One of the most popular therapies for anxiety is Cognitive Behavioral Therapy, which serves as an influence for this book. While CBT is complex and has many aspects, one fundamental tenet is that it helps an anxious person pinpoint unhelpful beliefs and behaviors and replace them with more objective facts and observations.

This book aims to help identify moments where you begin to feel anxious and think critically of yourself and gently guides them toward more compassionate and constructive thought patterns.

The exercises in this book are set up to be repeated multiple times as you deal with repeating episodes of feeling anxiety and self-criticism.

In this book, you will find many grounding and coping techniques. It starts with Self Assessments and a Prompts Planner to help you understand your anxiety and what you need to work on the most. You are then led into a Weekly Goal Tracking and Workout Planner to set physical and concrete goals for yourself. Followed by Daily Anxiety and Mindfulness Journal pages to help ease your busy mind and track your daily or hourly moods.

By the time you are done with this book, you will better understand your anxiety and what causes it, how to react and manage your anxiety, and how to be less anxious and have more control over your emotions.

Self Assessment

THE THINGS THAT BRING ME THE MOST JOY ARE:

THE ACTIVITIES THAT BRING ME THE MOST JOY ARE

THE PEOPLE THAT BRING ME THE MOST JOY ARE

Self Assessment

SELF CARE IS IMPORTANT TO ME BECAUSE

I CAN MAKE TIME FOR SELF CARE BY

I CAN DO THESE THINGS TO MAKE LIFE BETTER FOR MY FUTURE SELF

Self Assessment

I CAN DO THESE THINGS TO TAKE CART OF MY BODY

I CAN DO THESE THINGS TO TAKE CARE OF MY MIND

I CAN DO THESE THINGS TO TAKE CARE OF MY SOUL

Prompts *Planner*

What are three things you can do to help your mental health?

When times get tough I want to remember that...

No matter how terrible my day is, these can always make me feel better.

Prompts *Planner*

My best qualities are...

What are your best talents?

This month I'm looking for forward to...

Prompts Planner

The biggest lessons I've learned from anxiety are...

If I didn't have anxiety I would have never learned...

If I didn't have anxiety I would...

Prompts *Planner*

On a scale of 1 - 10 my mental health is at a ____ because...

Describe a situation where everything worked out for you.

What was your biggest failure and what did you learn from it?

Prompts *Planner*

Describe your biggest accomplishment.

What do you want more people to know own about you and why?

How do you want to be remembered?

Note's Planner

Weekly Tracking *Checklist*

CHECK IF DONE | **Week 1** | CHECK IF NOT DONE

GOAL 01

GOAL 02

GOAL 03

GOAL 04

GOAL 05

GOAL 06

NOTE'S

Workout *Planner*

Activity	Time	Reps
Day 1		
Day 2		
Day 3		
Day 4		
Day 5		
Day 6		

Anxiety Journal

Date: Sun   Mon   Tue   Wed   Thu   Fri   Sat

Goals for Today

Energy Level: ☆ ☆ ☆ ☆ ☆
Activity Level: ☆ ☆ ☆ ☆ ☆
Sleep Quality: ☆ ☆ ☆ ☆ ☆

Mood

◇ Happy   ◇ Stressed
◇ Hopeful   ◇ Sad
◇ Calm   ◇ _____
◇ Tired   ◇ _____

Stressed About

▪Triggers▪

Symptoms

Coping Skills

Notes

Mindfulness Journal

Date:......./......./.............   Sun Mon Tue Wed Thu Fri Sat

Todays Focus

I Want To Feel

Good Habits

My Inspiration

Self Care

Daily Task

☆_____
☆_____
☆_____
☆_____
☆_____

Today I am Grateful For _____

The Moment I Loved Was _____

Good Ideas

Notes

Anxiety Journal

Date: _____   Sun Mon Tue Wed Thu Fri Sat

Goals for Today

Energy Level: ☆ ☆ ☆ ☆ ☆

Activity Level: ☆ ☆ ☆ ☆ ☆

Sleep Quality: ☆ ☆ ☆ ☆ ☆

Mood

◇ Happy   ◇ Stressed
◇ Hopeful   ◇ Sad
◇ Calm   ◇ _____
◇ Tired   ◇ _____

Stressed About

▪Triggers▪

Symptoms

Coping Skills

Notes

Mindfulness Journal

Date:......./......./............   Sun Mon Tue Wed Thu Fri Sat

Todays Focus

_____
_____
_____

I Want To Feel

_____
_____
_____

Good Habits

_____
_____
_____
_____

My Inspiration

_____
_____
_____
_____

Self Care

- - - - - - - - - - - - - - - - -
- - - - - - - - - - - - - - - - -
- - - - - - - - - - - - - - - - -
- - - - - - - - - - - - - - - - -

Daily Task

☆ _____
☆ _____
☆ _____
☆ _____
☆ _____

Today I am Grateful For _____
_____

The Moment I Loved Was _____

Good Ideas

_____
_____
_____

Notes

_____
_____
_____

Anxiety Journal

Date: Sun Mon Tue Wed Thu Fri Sat

Goals for Today

Energy Level: ☆ ☆ ☆ ☆ ☆
Activity Level: ☆ ☆ ☆ ☆ ☆
Sleep Quality: ☆ ☆ ☆ ☆ ☆

Mood

◇ Happy   ◇ Stressed
◇ Hopeful   ◇ Sad
◇ Calm   ◇ _____
◇ Tired   ◇ _____

Stressed About

▪Triggers▪

Symptoms

Coping Skills

Notes

Mindfulness Journal

Date:....../......./............   Sun Mon Tue Wed Thu Fri Sat

Todays Focus

I Want To Feel

Good Habits

My Inspiration

Self Care

Daily Task

☆ _____
☆ _____
☆ _____
☆ _____
☆ _____

Today I am Grateful For _____

The Moment I Loved Was _____

Good Ideas

Notes

Anxiety Journal

Date: Sun   Mon   Tue   Wed   Thu   Fri   Sat

Goals for Today

Energy Level: ☆ ☆ ☆ ☆ ☆

Activity Level: ☆ ☆ ☆ ☆ ☆

Sleep Quality: ☆ ☆ ☆ ☆ ☆

Mood

◇ Happy   ◇ Stressed
◇ Hopeful   ◇ Sad
◇ Calm   ◇ _____
◇ Tired   ◇ _____

Stressed About

▪ Triggers ▪

Coping Skills

Symptoms

Notes

Mindfulness Journal

Date:......./......./............   Sun Mon Tue Wed Thu Fri Sat

Todays Focus

_____
_____
_____

I Want To Feel

_____
_____
_____

Good Habits

_____
_____
_____

My Inspiration

_____
_____
_____

Self Care

- - - - - - - - - - - - - - - - - - -
- - - - - - - - - - - - - - - - - - -
- - - - - - - - - - - - - - - - - - -

Daily Task

☆ _____
☆ _____
☆ _____
☆ _____
☆ _____

Today I am Grateful For _____

_____

The Moment I Loved Was _____

_____

Good Ideas

_____
_____
_____

Notes

_____
_____
_____

Anxiety Journal

Date: Sun   Mon   Tue   Wed   Thu   Fri   Sat

Goals for Today

Energy Level: ☆ ☆ ☆ ☆ ☆

Activity Level: ☆ ☆ ☆ ☆ ☆

Sleep Quality: ☆ ☆ ☆ ☆ ☆

Mood

◇ Happy   ◇ Stressed

◇ Hopeful   ◇ Sad

◇ Calm   ◇ _____

◇ Tired   ◇ _____

Stressed About

▪ Triggers ▪

Coping Skills

Symptoms

Notes

Mindfulness Journal

Date:......./......./..............   Sun Mon Tue Wed Thu Fri Sat

Todays Focus

I Want To Feel

Good Habits

My Inspiration

Self Care

Daily Task

☆ _____
☆ _____
☆ _____
☆ _____
☆ _____

Today I am Grateful For _____

The Moment I Loved Was _____

Good Ideas

Notes

Anxiety Journal

Date: Sun   Mon   Tue   Wed   Thu   Fri   Sat

Goals for Today

Energy Level: ☆ ☆ ☆ ☆ ☆

Activity Level: ☆ ☆ ☆ ☆ ☆

Sleep Quality: ☆ ☆ ☆ ☆ ☆

Mood

◇ Happy   ◇ Stressed

◇ Hopeful   ◇ Sad

◇ Calm   ◇ _____

◇ Tired   ◇ _____

Stressed About

■ Triggers ■

Coping Skills

Symptoms

Notes

Mindfulness Journal

Date:......./......./............   Sun Mon Tue Wed Thu Fri Sat

Todays Focus

I Want To Feel

Good Habits

My Inspiration

Self Care

Daily Task

☆ _____
☆ _____
☆ _____
☆ _____
☆ _____

Today I am Grateful For _____

The Moment I Loved Was _____

Good Ideas

Notes

Anxiety Journal

Date: Sun   Mon   Tue   Wed   Thu   Fri   Sat

Goals for Today

Energy Level: ☆ ☆ ☆ ☆ ☆

Activity Level: ☆ ☆ ☆ ☆ ☆

Sleep Quality: ☆ ☆ ☆ ☆ ☆

Mood

◇ Happy   ◇ Stressed

◇ Hopeful   ◇ Sad

◇ Calm   ◇ _____

◇ Tired   ◇ _____

Stressed About

▪Triggers▪

Symptoms

Coping Skills

Notes

Mindfulness Journal

Date:......./......./............   Sun Mon Tue Wed Thu Fri Sat

Todays Focus

I Want To Feel

Good Habits

My Inspiration

Self Care

Daily Task

☆ _____
☆ _____
☆ _____
☆ _____
☆ _____

Today I am Grateful For _____

The Moment I Loved Was _____

Good Ideas

Notes

Weekly Tracking *Checklist*

Week 2

GOAL 01

GOAL 02

GOAL 03

GOAL 04

GOAL 05

GOAL 06

NOTE'S

Workout *Planner*

Activity	Time	Reps
Day 1		
Day 2		
Day 3		
Day 4		
Day 5		
Day 6		

Anxiety Journal

Date: Sun   Mon   Tue   Wed   Thu   Fri   Sat

Goals for Today

Energy Level: ☆ ☆ ☆ ☆ ☆

Activity Level: ☆ ☆ ☆ ☆ ☆

Sleep Quality: ☆ ☆ ☆ ☆ ☆

Mood

◇ Happy   ◇ Stressed

◇ Hopeful   ◇ Sad

◇ Calm   ◇ _____

◇ Tired   ◇ _____

Stressed About

■Triggers■

Symptoms

Coping Skills

Notes

Mindfulness Journal

Date:......./......./.............   Sun Mon Tue Wed Thu Fri Sat

Todays Focus

_____
_____
_____

I Want To Feel

_____
_____
_____

Good Habits

_____
_____
_____
_____

My Inspiration

_____
_____
_____
_____

Self Care

- - - - - - - - - - - - - - - -
- - - - - - - - - - - - - - - -
- - - - - - - - - - - - - - - -
- - - - - - - - - - - - - - - -
- - - - - - - - - - - - - - - -

Daily Task

☆ _____
☆ _____
☆ _____
☆ _____
☆ _____

Today I am Grateful For _____

_____

The Moment I Loved Was _____

_____

Good Ideas

_____
_____
_____

Notes

_____
_____
_____

Anxiety Journal

Date: Sun   Mon   Tue   Wed   Thu   Fri   Sat

Goals for Today

Energy Level: ☆ ☆ ☆ ☆ ☆

Activity Level: ☆ ☆ ☆ ☆ ☆

Sleep Quality: ☆ ☆ ☆ ☆ ☆

Mood

◇ Happy   ◇ Stressed

◇ Hopeful   ◇ Sad

◇ Calm   ◇ _____

◇ Tired   ◇ _____

Stressed About

▪ Triggers ▪

Symptoms

Coping Skills

Notes

Mindfulness Journal

Date:....../......./............   Sun Mon Tue Wed Thu Fri Sat

Todays Focus

I Want To Feel

Good Habits

My Inspiration

Self Care

Daily Task

☆_____
☆_____
☆_____
☆_____
☆_____

Today I am Grateful For _____

_____

The Moment I Loved Was _____

_____

Good Ideas

Notes

Anxiety Journal

Date: Sun Mon Tue Wed Thu Fri Sat

Goals for Today

Energy Level: ☆ ☆ ☆ ☆ ☆

Activity Level: ☆ ☆ ☆ ☆ ☆

Sleep Quality: ☆ ☆ ☆ ☆ ☆

Mood

◇ Happy   ◇ Stressed

◇ Hopeful   ◇ Sad

◇ Calm   ◇ _____

◇ Tired   ◇ _____

Stressed About

▪Triggers▪

Symptoms

Coping Skills

Notes

Mindfulness Journal

Date:......./......./............   Sun Mon Tue Wed Thu Fri Sat

Todays Focus

_____
_____
_____

I Want To Feel

_____
_____
_____

Good Habits

_____
_____
_____
_____

My Inspiration

_____
_____
_____
_____

Self Care

- - - - - - - - - - - -
- - - - - - - - - - - -
- - - - - - - - - - - -
- - - - - - - - - - - -
- - - - - - - - - - - -

Daily Task

☆ _____
☆ _____
☆ _____
☆ _____
☆ _____

Today I am Grateful For _____

_____

The Moment I Loved Was _____

_____

Good Ideas

_____
_____
_____

Notes

_____
_____
_____

Anxiety Journal

Date: Sun Mon Tue Wed Thu Fri Sat

Goals for Today

Energy Level: ☆ ☆ ☆ ☆ ☆
Activity Level: ☆ ☆ ☆ ☆ ☆
Sleep Quality: ☆ ☆ ☆ ☆ ☆

Mood

◇ Happy   ◇ Stressed
◇ Hopeful   ◇ Sad
◇ Calm   ◇ _____
◇ Tired   ◇ _____

Stressed About

■ Triggers ■

Symptoms

Coping Skills

Notes

Mindfulness Journal

Date:........../.........../.............   Sun Mon Tue Wed Thu Fri Sat

Todays Focus

I Want To Feel

Good Habits

My Inspiration

Self Care

Daily Task

☆ _____
☆ _____
☆ _____
☆ _____
☆ _____

Today I am Grateful For _____

The Moment I Loved Was _____

Good Ideas

Notes

Anxiety Journal

Date: Sun   Mon   Tue   Wed   Thu   Fri   Sat

Goals for Today

Energy Level: ☆ ☆ ☆ ☆ ☆
Activity Level: ☆ ☆ ☆ ☆ ☆
Sleep Quality: ☆ ☆ ☆ ☆ ☆

Mood

◇ Happy   ◇ Stressed
◇ Hopeful   ◇ Sad
◇ Calm   ◇ _____
◇ Tired   ◇ _____

Stressed About

▪Triggers▪

Symptoms

Coping Skills

Notes

Mindfulness Journal

Date:....../......./............   Sun Mon Tue Wed Thu Fri Sat

Todays Focus

_____
_____
_____

I Want To Feel

_____
_____
_____

Good Habits

_____
_____
_____

My Inspiration

_____
_____
_____

Self Care

- - - - - - - - - - - - - - - -
- - - - - - - - - - - - - - - -
- - - - - - - - - - - - - - - -
- - - - - - - - - - - - - - - -

Daily Task

☆ _____
☆ _____
☆ _____
☆ _____
☆ _____

Today I am Grateful For _____
_____

The Moment I Loved Was _____
_____

Good Ideas

_____
_____
_____

Notes

_____
_____
_____

Anxiety Journal

Date: Sun   Mon   Tue   Wed   Thu   Fri   Sat

Goals for Today

Energy Level: ☆ ☆ ☆ ☆ ☆

Activity Level: ☆ ☆ ☆ ☆ ☆

Sleep Quality: ☆ ☆ ☆ ☆ ☆

Mood

◇ Happy   ◇ Stressed

◇ Hopeful   ◇ Sad

◇ Calm   ◇ _____

◇ Tired   ◇ _____

Stressed About

▪Triggers▪

Symptoms

Coping Skills

Notes

Mindfulness Journal

Date:......./......./............   Sun Mon Tue Wed Thu Fri Sat

Todays Focus

I Want To Feel

Good Habits

My Inspiration

Self Care

Daily Task

☆ _____
☆ _____
☆ _____
☆ _____
☆ _____

Today I am Grateful For _____

The Moment I Loved Was _____

Good Ideas

Notes

Anxiety Journal

Date: Sun   Mon   Tue   Wed   Thu   Fri   Sat

Goals for Today

Energy Level: ☆ ☆ ☆ ☆ ☆

Activity Level: ☆ ☆ ☆ ☆ ☆

Sleep Quality: ☆ ☆ ☆ ☆ ☆

Mood

◇ Happy   ◇ Stressed

◇ Hopeful   ◇ Sad

◇ Calm   ◇ _____

◇ Tired   ◇ _____

Stressed About

▪ Triggers ▪

Symptoms

Coping Skills

Notes

Mindfulness Journal

Date:......../........./...............   Sun Mon Tue Wed Thu Fri Sat

Todays Focus

I Want To Feel

Good Habits

My Inspiration

Self Care

Daily Task

☆ _____
☆ _____
☆ _____
☆ _____
☆ _____

Today I am Grateful For _____

The Moment I Loved Was _____

Good Ideas

Notes

Weekly Tracking *Checklist*

Week 3

GOAL 01

GOAL 02

GOAL 03

GOAL 04

GOAL 05

GOAL 06

NOTE'S

Workout *Planner*

Activity	Time	Reps
Day 1		
Day 2		
Day 3		
Day 4		
Day 5		
Day 6		

Anxiety Journal

Date: Sun   Mon   Tue   Wed   Thu   Fri   Sat

Goals for Today

Energy Level: ☆ ☆ ☆ ☆ ☆

Activity Level: ☆ ☆ ☆ ☆ ☆

Sleep Quality: ☆ ☆ ☆ ☆ ☆

Mood

◇ Happy   ◇ Stressed

◇ Hopeful   ◇ Sad

◇ Calm   ◇ _____

◇ Tired   ◇ _____

Stressed About

▪Triggers▪

Symptoms

Coping Skills

Notes

Mindfulness Journal

Date:....../....../............   Sun Mon Tue Wed Thu Fri Sat

Todays Focus

I Want To Feel

Good Habits

My Inspiration

Self Care

Daily Task

☆ _____
☆ _____
☆ _____
☆ _____
☆ _____

Today I am Grateful For _____

The Moment I Loved Was _____

Good Ideas

Notes

Anxiety Journal

Date: | Sun Mon Tue Wed Thu Fri Sat

Goals for Today

Energy Level: ☆ ☆ ☆ ☆ ☆
Activity Level: ☆ ☆ ☆ ☆ ☆
Sleep Quality: ☆ ☆ ☆ ☆ ☆

Mood

◇ Happy   ◇ Stressed
◇ Hopeful   ◇ Sad
◇ Calm   ◇ _____
◇ Tired   ◇ _____

Stressed About

▪Triggers▪

Symptoms

Coping Skills

Notes

Mindfulness Journal

Date:......./......../............   Sun Mon Tue Wed Thu Fri Sat

Todays Focus

I Want To Feel

Good Habits

My Inspiration

Self Care

Daily Task

☆_____
☆_____
☆_____
☆_____
☆_____

Today I am Grateful For _____

_____

The Moment I Loved Was _____

_____

Good Ideas

Notes

Anxiety Journal

Date: Sun Mon Tue Wed Thu Fri Sat

Goals for Today

Energy Level: ☆ ☆ ☆ ☆ ☆

Activity Level: ☆ ☆ ☆ ☆ ☆

Sleep Quality: ☆ ☆ ☆ ☆ ☆

Mood

◇ Happy   ◇ Stressed

◇ Hopeful   ◇ Sad

◇ Calm   ◇ _____

◇ Tired   ◇ _____

Stressed About

■ Triggers ■

Symptoms

Coping Skills

Notes

Mindfulness Journal

Date:......./......./...........   Sun Mon Tue Wed Thu Fri Sat

Todays Focus

I Want To Feel

Good Habits

My Inspiration

Self Care

Daily Task

☆ _____
☆ _____
☆ _____
☆ _____
☆ _____

Today I am Grateful For _____

_____

The Moment I Loved Was _____

Good Ideas

Notes

Anxiety Journal

Date: Sun Mon Tue Wed Thu Fri Sat

Goals for Today

Energy Level: ☆ ☆ ☆ ☆ ☆

Activity Level: ☆ ☆ ☆ ☆ ☆

Sleep Quality: ☆ ☆ ☆ ☆ ☆

Mood

◇ Happy   ◇ Stressed
◇ Hopeful   ◇ Sad
◇ Calm   ◇ _____
◇ Tired   ◇ _____

Stressed About

▪Triggers▪

Symptoms

Coping Skills

Notes

Mindfulness Journal

Date:......./........./............   Sun Mon Tue Wed Thu Fri Sat

Todays Focus

I Want To Feel

Good Habits

My Inspiration

Self Care

- - - - - - - - - - - - - - - - -
- - - - - - - - - - - - - - - - -
- - - - - - - - - - - - - - - - -
- - - - - - - - - - - - - - - - -
- - - - - - - - - - - - - - - - -

Daily Task

☆ _____
☆ _____
☆ _____
☆ _____
☆ _____

Today I am Grateful For _____

The Moment I Loved Was _____

Good Ideas

Notes

Anxiety Journal

Date: _____ Sun Mon Tue Wed Thu Fri Sat

Goals for Today

Energy Level: ☆ ☆ ☆ ☆ ☆

Activity Level: ☆ ☆ ☆ ☆ ☆

Sleep Quality: ☆ ☆ ☆ ☆ ☆

Mood

◇ Happy   ◇ Stressed
◇ Hopeful   ◇ Sad
◇ Calm   ◇ _____
◇ Tired   ◇ _____

Stressed About

▪Triggers▪

Symptoms

Coping Skills

Notes

Mindfulness Journal

Date:......./......./............   Sun Mon Tue Wed Thu Fri Sat

Todays Focus

I Want To Feel

Good Habits

My Inspiration

Self Care

Daily Task

☆_____
☆_____
☆_____
☆_____
☆_____

Today I am Grateful For _____

_____

The Moment I Loved Was _____

_____

Good Ideas

Notes

Anxiety Journal

Date: Sun   Mon   Tue   Wed   Thu   Fri   Sat

Goals for Today

Energy Level: ☆ ☆ ☆ ☆ ☆
Activity Level: ☆ ☆ ☆ ☆ ☆
Sleep Quality: ☆ ☆ ☆ ☆ ☆

Mood

◇ Happy   ◇ Stressed
◇ Hopeful   ◇ Sad
◇ Calm   ◇ _____
◇ Tired   ◇ _____

Stressed About

▪ Triggers ▪

Symptoms

Coping Skills

Notes

Mindfulness Journal

Date:......./......../............   Sun Mon Tue Wed Thu Fri Sat

Todays Focus

I Want To Feel

Good Habits

My Inspiration

Self Care

Daily Task

☆ _____
☆ _____
☆ _____
☆ _____
☆ _____

Today I am Grateful For _____

The Moment I Loved Was _____

Good Ideas

Notes

Anxiety Journal

Date: Sun   Mon   Tue   Wed   Thu   Fri   Sat

Goals for Today

Energy Level: ☆ ☆ ☆ ☆ ☆

Activity Level: ☆ ☆ ☆ ☆ ☆

Sleep Quality: ☆ ☆ ☆ ☆ ☆

Mood

◇ Happy   ◇ Stressed

◇ Hopeful   ◇ Sad

◇ Calm   ◇ _____

◇ Tired   ◇ _____

Stressed About

▪ Triggers ▪

Coping Skills

Symptoms

Notes

Mindfulness Journal

Date:........./........./............   Sun Mon Tue Wed Thu Fri Sat

Todays Focus

I Want To Feel

Good Habits

My Inspiration

Self Care

- — — — — — — — — — —
- — — — — — — — — — —
- — — — — — — — — — —
- — — — — — — — — — —
- — — — — — — — — — —

Daily Task

☆ _____
☆ _____
☆ _____
☆ _____
☆ _____

Today I am Grateful For _____

The Moment I Loved Was _____

Good Ideas

Notes

Weekly Tracking *Checklist*

Week 4

GOAL 01

GOAL 02

GOAL 03

GOAL 04

GOAL 05

GOAL 06

NOTE'S

Workout *Planner*

Activity	Time	Reps

	Activity	Time	Reps
Day 1			
Day 2			
Day 3			
Day 4			
Day 5			
Day 6			

Anxiety Journal

Date: Sun   Mon   Tue   Wed   Thu   Fri   Sat

Goals for Today

Energy Level: ☆ ☆ ☆ ☆ ☆

Activity Level: ☆ ☆ ☆ ☆ ☆

Sleep Quality: ☆ ☆ ☆ ☆ ☆

Mood

◇ Happy   ◇ Stressed
◇ Hopeful   ◇ Sad
◇ Calm   ◇ _____
◇ Tired   ◇ _____

Stressed About

Triggers

Symptoms

Coping Skills

Notes

Mindfulness Journal

Date:......./......../..............   Sun Mon Tue Wed Thu Fri Sat

Todays Focus

_____
_____
_____

I Want To Feel

_____
_____
_____

Good Habits

_____
_____
_____

My Inspiration

_____
_____
_____

Self Care

- - - - - - - - - - - - - - - - -
- - - - - - - - - - - - - - - - -
- - - - - - - - - - - - - - - - -
- - - - - - - - - - - - - - - - -
- - - - - - - - - - - - - - - - -

Daily Task

☆ _____
☆ _____
☆ _____
☆ _____
☆ _____

Today I am Grateful For _____
_____

The Moment I Loved Was _____
_____

Good Ideas

_____
_____
_____

Notes

_____
_____
_____

Anxiety Journal

Date: _____ Sun Mon Tue Wed Thu Fri Sat

Goals for Today

Energy Level: ☆ ☆ ☆ ☆ ☆

Activity Level: ☆ ☆ ☆ ☆ ☆

Sleep Quality: ☆ ☆ ☆ ☆ ☆

Mood

◇ Happy   ◇ Stressed
◇ Hopeful   ◇ Sad
◇ Calm   ◇ _____
◇ Tired   ◇ _____

Stressed About

Triggers

Symptoms

Coping Skills

Notes

Mindfulness Journal

Date:......../........./............   Sun Mon Tue Wed Thu Fri Sat

Todays Focus

_____
_____
_____

I Want To Feel

_____
_____
_____

Good Habits

_____
_____
_____
_____

My Inspiration

_____
_____
_____
_____

Self Care

- - - - - - - - - - - - - - - -
- - - - - - - - - - - - - - - -
- - - - - - - - - - - - - - - -
- - - - - - - - - - - - - - - -
- - - - - - - - - - - - - - - -

Daily Task

☆ _____
☆ _____
☆ _____
☆ _____
☆ _____

Today I am Grateful For _____
_____

The Moment I Loved Was _____
_____

Good Ideas

_____
_____
_____
_____

Notes

_____
_____
_____
_____

Anxiety Journal

Date: _____ Sun Mon Tue Wed Thu Fri Sat

Goals for Today

Energy Level: ☆ ☆ ☆ ☆ ☆

Activity Level: ☆ ☆ ☆ ☆ ☆

Sleep Quality: ☆ ☆ ☆ ☆ ☆

Mood

◇ Happy   ◇ Stressed
◇ Hopeful   ◇ Sad
◇ Calm   ◇ _____
◇ Tired   ◇ _____

Stressed About

▪Triggers▪

Symptoms

Coping Skills

Notes

Mindfulness Journal

Date:........./........./................   Sun Mon Tue Wed Thu Fri Sat

Todays Focus

I Want To Feel

Good Habits

My Inspiration

Self Care

Daily Task

☆ _____
☆ _____
☆ _____
☆ _____
☆ _____

Today I am Grateful For _____

The Moment I Loved Was _____

Good Ideas

Notes

Anxiety Journal

Date: Sun   Mon   Tue   Wed   Thu   Fri   Sat

Goals for Today

Energy Level: ☆ ☆ ☆ ☆ ☆

Activity Level: ☆ ☆ ☆ ☆ ☆

Sleep Quality: ☆ ☆ ☆ ☆ ☆

Mood

◇ Happy   ◇ Stressed

◇ Hopeful   ◇ Sad

◇ Calm   ◇ _____

◇ Tired   ◇ _____

Stressed About

▪Triggers▪

Symptoms

Coping Skills

Notes

Mindfulness Journal

Date:......./......./............   Sun Mon Tue Wed Thu Fri Sat

Todays Focus

I Want To Feel

Good Habits

My Inspiration

Self Care

Daily Task

☆ _____
☆ _____
☆ _____
☆ _____
☆ _____

Today I am Grateful For _____

The Moment I Loved Was _____

Good Ideas

Notes

Anxiety Journal

Date: _____ Sun Mon Tue Wed Thu Fri Sat

Goals for Today

Energy Level: ☆ ☆ ☆ ☆ ☆

Activity Level: ☆ ☆ ☆ ☆ ☆

Sleep Quality: ☆ ☆ ☆ ☆ ☆

Mood

◇ Happy   ◇ Stressed
◇ Hopeful   ◇ Sad
◇ Calm   ◇ _____
◇ Tired   ◇ _____

Stressed About

▪Triggers▪

Symptoms

Coping Skills

Notes

Mindfulness Journal

Date:......./......./............   Sun Mon Tue Wed Thu Fri Sat

Todays Focus

I Want To Feel

Good Habits

My Inspiration

Self Care

Daily Task

☆ _____
☆ _____
☆ _____
☆ _____
☆ _____

Today I am Grateful For _____

The Moment I Loved Was _____

Good Ideas

Notes

Anxiety Journal

Date: Sun Mon Tue Wed Thu Fri Sat

Goals for Today

Energy Level: ☆ ☆ ☆ ☆ ☆

Activity Level: ☆ ☆ ☆ ☆ ☆

Sleep Quality: ☆ ☆ ☆ ☆ ☆

Mood

◇ Happy   ◇ Stressed
◇ Hopeful   ◇ Sad
◇ Calm   ◇ _____
◇ Tired   ◇ _____

Stressed About

▪Triggers▪

Symptoms

Coping Skills

Notes

Mindfulness Journal

Date:......./......./.............   Sun Mon Tue Wed Thu Fri Sat

Todays Focus

I Want To Feel

Good Habits

My Inspiration

Self Care

Daily Task

☆_____
☆_____
☆_____
☆_____
☆_____

Today I am Grateful For _____

_____

The Moment I Loved Was _____

_____

Good Ideas

Notes

Anxiety Journal

Date: _____ Sun Mon Tue Wed Thu Fri Sat

Goals for Today

Energy Level: ☆ ☆ ☆ ☆ ☆

Activity Level: ☆ ☆ ☆ ☆ ☆

Sleep Quality: ☆ ☆ ☆ ☆ ☆

Mood

◇ Happy   ◇ Stressed
◇ Hopeful   ◇ Sad
◇ Calm   ◇ _____
◇ Tired   ◇ _____

Stressed About

▪Triggers▪

Symptoms

Coping Skills

Notes

Mindfulness Journal

Date:......./......../.............   Sun Mon Tue Wed Thu Fri Sat

Todays Focus

_____
_____
_____

I Want To Feel

_____
_____
_____

Good Habits

_____
_____
_____

My Inspiration

_____
_____
_____

Self Care

- - - - - - - - - - - - - - - -
- - - - - - - - - - - - - - - -
- - - - - - - - - - - - - - - -
- - - - - - - - - - - - - - - -

Daily Task

☆ _____
☆ _____
☆ _____
☆ _____
☆ _____

Today I am Grateful For _____

_____

The Moment I Loved Was _____

Good Ideas

_____
_____
_____

Notes

_____
_____
_____

Weekly Tracking *Checklist*

Week 5

GOAL 01

GOAL 02

GOAL 03

GOAL 04

GOAL 05

GOAL 06

NOTE'S

Workout *Planner*

Activity	Time	Reps

Day 1

Day 2

Day 3

Day 4

Day 5

Day 6

Anxiety Journal

Date: Sun Mon Tue Wed Thu Fri Sat

Goals for Today

Energy Level: ☆ ☆ ☆ ☆ ☆

Activity Level: ☆ ☆ ☆ ☆ ☆

Sleep Quality: ☆ ☆ ☆ ☆ ☆

Mood

◇ Happy   ◇ Stressed

◇ Hopeful   ◇ Sad

◇ Calm   ◇ _____

◇ Tired   ◇ _____

Stressed About

▪Triggers▪

Symptoms

Coping Skills

Notes

Mindfulness Journal

Date:......./........./.............   Sun Mon Tue Wed Thu Fri Sat

Todays Focus

I Want To Feel

Good Habits

My Inspiration

Self Care

Daily Task

☆ _____
☆ _____
☆ _____
☆ _____
☆ _____

Today I am Grateful For _____

The Moment I Loved Was _____

Good Ideas

Notes

Anxiety Journal

Date: _____ Sun Mon Tue Wed Thu Fri Sat

Goals for Today

Energy Level: ☆ ☆ ☆ ☆ ☆

Activity Level: ☆ ☆ ☆ ☆ ☆

Sleep Quality: ☆ ☆ ☆ ☆ ☆

Mood

◇ Happy   ◇ Stressed
◇ Hopeful   ◇ Sad
◇ Calm   ◇ _____
◇ Tired   ◇ _____

Stressed About

▪Triggers▪

Symptoms

Coping Skills

Notes

Mindfulness Journal

Date:......./......./.............   Sun Mon Tue Wed Thu Fri Sat

Todays Focus

I Want To Feel

Good Habits

My Inspiration

Self Care

Daily Task

☆ _____
☆ _____
☆ _____
☆ _____
☆ _____

Today I am Grateful For _____

_____

The Moment I Loved Was _____

_____

Good Ideas

Notes

Anxiety Journal

Date: _____ Sun Mon Tue Wed Thu Fri Sat

Goals for Today

Energy Level: ☆ ☆ ☆ ☆ ☆

Activity Level: ☆ ☆ ☆ ☆ ☆

Sleep Quality: ☆ ☆ ☆ ☆ ☆

Mood

◇ Happy   ◇ Stressed

◇ Hopeful   ◇ Sad

◇ Calm   ◇ _____

◇ Tired   ◇ _____

Stressed About

▪ Triggers ▪

Symptoms

Coping Skills

Notes

Mindfulness Journal

Date:......../........./............   Sun Mon Tue Wed Thu Fri Sat

Todays Focus

I Want To Feel

Good Habits

My Inspiration

Self Care

Daily Task

☆ _____
☆ _____
☆ _____
☆ _____
☆ _____

Today I am Grateful For _____

_____

The Moment I Loved Was _____

_____

Good Ideas

Notes

Anxiety Journal

Date: _____ Sun Mon Tue Wed Thu Fri Sat

Goals for Today

Energy Level: ☆ ☆ ☆ ☆ ☆

Activity Level: ☆ ☆ ☆ ☆ ☆

Sleep Quality: ☆ ☆ ☆ ☆ ☆

Mood

◇ Happy   ◇ Stressed
◇ Hopeful ◇ Sad
◇ Calm   ◇ _____
◇ Tired   ◇ _____

Stressed About

■ Triggers ■

Symptoms

Coping Skills

Notes

Mindfulness Journal

Date:......./......./............   Sun Mon Tue Wed Thu Fri Sat

Todays Focus

I Want To Feel

Good Habits

My Inspiration

Self Care

- - - - - - - - - - - - - - -
- - - - - - - - - - - - - - -
- - - - - - - - - - - - - - -
- - - - - - - - - - - - - - -

Daily Task

☆ _____
☆ _____
☆ _____
☆ _____
☆ _____

Today I am Grateful For _____

_____

The Moment I Loved Was _____

_____

Good Ideas

Notes

Anxiety Journal

Date: Sun   Mon   Tue   Wed   Thu   Fri   Sat

Goals for Today

Energy Level: ☆ ☆ ☆ ☆ ☆

Activity Level: ☆ ☆ ☆ ☆ ☆

Sleep Quality: ☆ ☆ ☆ ☆ ☆

Mood

◇ Happy   ◇ Stressed
◇ Hopeful   ◇ Sad
◇ Calm   ◇ _____
◇ Tired   ◇ _____

Stressed About

▪Triggers▪

Symptoms

Coping Skills

Notes

Mindfulness Journal

Date:......./......../............   Sun Mon Tue Wed Thu Fri Sat

Todays Focus

I Want To Feel

Good Habits

My Inspiration

Self Care

Daily Task

☆_____
☆_____
☆_____
☆_____
☆_____

Today I am Grateful For _____

_____

The Moment I Loved Was _____

_____

Good Ideas

Notes

Anxiety Journal

Date: Sun Mon Tue Wed Thu Fri Sat

Goals for Today

Energy Level: ☆ ☆ ☆ ☆ ☆
Activity Level: ☆ ☆ ☆ ☆ ☆
Sleep Quality: ☆ ☆ ☆ ☆ ☆

Mood

◇ Happy   ◇ Stressed
◇ Hopeful   ◇ Sad
◇ Calm   ◇ _____
◇ Tired   ◇ _____

Stressed About

▪Triggers▪

Symptoms

Coping Skills

Notes

Mindfulness Journal

Date:......./........./............   Sun Mon Tue Wed Thu Fri Sat

Todays Focus

_____
_____
_____

I Want To Feel

_____
_____
_____

Good Habits

_____
_____
_____

My Inspiration

_____
_____
_____
_____

Self Care

- - - - - - - - - - - - - - -
- - - - - - - - - - - - - - -
- - - - - - - - - - - - - - -
- - - - - - - - - - - - - - -
- - - - - - - - - - - - - - -

Daily Task

☆ _____
☆ _____
☆ _____
☆ _____
☆ _____

Today I am Grateful For _____
_____

The Moment I Loved Was _____
_____

Good Ideas

_____
_____
_____

Notes

_____
_____
_____

Anxiety Journal

Date: Sun Mon Tue Wed Thu Fri Sat

Goals for Today

Energy Level: ☆ ☆ ☆ ☆ ☆

Activity Level: ☆ ☆ ☆ ☆ ☆

Sleep Quality: ☆ ☆ ☆ ☆ ☆

Mood

◇ Happy   ◇ Stressed

◇ Hopeful   ◇ Sad

◇ Calm   ◇ _____

◇ Tired   ◇ _____

Stressed About

▪Triggers▪

Symptoms

Coping Skills

Notes

Mindfulness Journal

Date:......./......./.............   Sun Mon Tue Wed Thu Fri Sat

Todays Focus

I Want To Feel

Good Habits

My Inspiration

Self Care

Daily Task

☆ _____
☆ _____
☆ _____
☆ _____
☆ _____

Today I am Grateful For _____

_____

The Moment I Loved Was _____

_____

Good Ideas

Notes

Weekly Tracking *Checklist*

GOAL 01

GOAL 02

GOAL 03

GOAL 04

GOAL 05

GOAL 06

NOTE'S

Workout *Planner*

Activity	Time	Reps
Day 1		
Day 2		
Day 3		
Day 4		
Day 5		
Day 6		

Anxiety Journal

Date: Sun   Mon   Tue   Wed   Thu   Fri   Sat

Goals for Today

Energy Level: ☆ ☆ ☆ ☆ ☆
Activity Level: ☆ ☆ ☆ ☆ ☆
Sleep Quality: ☆ ☆ ☆ ☆ ☆

Mood

◇ Happy   ◇ Stressed
◇ Hopeful   ◇ Sad
◇ Calm   ◇ _____
◇ Tired   ◇ _____

Stressed About

▪ Triggers ▪

Symptoms

Coping Skills

Notes

Mindfulness Journal

Date:......../......../.............   Sun Mon Tue Wed Thu Fri Sat

Todays Focus

I Want To Feel

Good Habits

My Inspiration

Self Care

Daily Task

☆ _____
☆ _____
☆ _____
☆ _____
☆ _____

Today I am Grateful For _____

_____

The Moment I Loved Was _____

_____

Good Ideas

Notes

Anxiety Journal

Date: | Sun Mon Tue Wed Thu Fri Sat

Goals for Today

Energy Level: ☆ ☆ ☆ ☆ ☆

Activity Level: ☆ ☆ ☆ ☆ ☆

Sleep Quality: ☆ ☆ ☆ ☆ ☆

Mood

◇ Happy   ◇ Stressed
◇ Hopeful   ◇ Sad
◇ Calm   ◇ _____
◇ Tired   ◇ _____

Stressed About

▪Triggers▪

Symptoms

Coping Skills

Notes

Mindfulness Journal

Date:......./......../............   Sun Mon Tue Wed Thu Fri Sat

Todays Focus

_____
_____
_____

I Want To Feel

_____
_____
_____

Good Habits

_____
_____
_____
_____

My Inspiration

_____
_____
_____
_____

Self Care

- - - - - - - - - - - - - - -
- - - - - - - - - - - - - - -
- - - - - - - - - - - - - - -
- - - - - - - - - - - - - - -

Daily Task

☆ _____
☆ _____
☆ _____
☆ _____
☆ _____

Today I am Grateful For _____
_____

The Moment I Loved Was _____
_____

Good Ideas

_____
_____
_____

Notes

_____
_____
_____

Anxiety Journal

Date: Sun Mon Tue Wed Thu Fri Sat

Goals for Today

Energy Level: ☆ ☆ ☆ ☆ ☆
Activity Level: ☆ ☆ ☆ ☆ ☆
Sleep Quality: ☆ ☆ ☆ ☆ ☆

Mood

◇ Happy   ◇ Stressed
◇ Hopeful   ◇ Sad
◇ Calm   ◇ _____
◇ Tired   ◇ _____

Stressed About

▪Triggers▪

Symptoms

Coping Skills

Notes

Mindfulness Journal

Date:......./........./............   Sun Mon Tue Wed Thu Fri Sat

Todays Focus

I Want To Feel

Good Habits

My Inspiration

Self Care

Daily Task

☆ _____
☆ _____
☆ _____
☆ _____
☆ _____

Today I am Grateful For _____

_____

The Moment I Loved Was _____

_____

Good Ideas

Notes

Anxiety Journal

Date: Sun   Mon   Tue   Wed   Thu   Fri   Sat

Goals for Today

Energy Level: ☆ ☆ ☆ ☆ ☆

Activity Level: ☆ ☆ ☆ ☆ ☆

Sleep Quality: ☆ ☆ ☆ ☆ ☆

Mood

◇ Happy   ◇ Stressed

◇ Hopeful   ◇ Sad

◇ Calm   ◇ _____

◇ Tired   ◇ _____

Stressed About

■ Triggers ■

Symptoms

Coping Skills

Notes

Mindfulness Journal

Date:......./........./.............   Sun Mon Tue Wed Thu Fri Sat

Todays Focus

_____
_____
_____

I Want To Feel

_____
_____
_____

Good Habits

_____
_____
_____

My Inspiration

_____
_____
_____

Self Care

- - - - - - - - - - - -
- - - - - - - - - - - -
- - - - - - - - - - - -
- - - - - - - - - - - -
- - - - - - - - - - - -

Daily Task

☆ _____
☆ _____
☆ _____
☆ _____
☆ _____

Today I am Grateful For _____

_____

The Moment I Loved Was _____

_____

Good Ideas

_____
_____
_____

Notes

_____
_____
_____

Anxiety Journal

Date: Sun   Mon   Tue   Wed   Thu   Fri   Sat

Goals for Today

Energy Level: ☆ ☆ ☆ ☆ ☆

Activity Level: ☆ ☆ ☆ ☆ ☆

Sleep Quality: ☆ ☆ ☆ ☆ ☆

Mood

◇ Happy   ◇ Stressed

◇ Hopeful   ◇ Sad

◇ Calm   ◇ _____

◇ Tired   ◇ _____

Stressed About

▪Triggers▪

Symptoms

Coping Skills

Notes

Mindfulness Journal

Date:........./........./...............   Sun Mon Tue Wed Thu Fri Sat

Todays Focus

I Want To Feel

Good Habits

My Inspiration

Self Care

Daily Task

☆ _____
☆ _____
☆ _____
☆ _____
☆ _____

Today I am Grateful For _____

_____

The Moment I Loved Was _____

_____

Good Ideas

Notes

Anxiety Journal

Date: Sun   Mon   Tue   Wed   Thu   Fri   Sat

Goals for Today

Energy Level: ☆ ☆ ☆ ☆ ☆

Activity Level: ☆ ☆ ☆ ☆ ☆

Sleep Quality: ☆ ☆ ☆ ☆ ☆

Mood

◇ Happy   ◇ Stressed

◇ Hopeful   ◇ Sad

◇ Calm   ◇ _____

◇ Tired   ◇ _____

Stressed About

▪ Triggers ▪

Coping Skills

Symptoms

Notes

Mindfulness Journal

Date:......./........./............   Sun Mon Tue Wed Thu Fri Sat

Todays Focus

I Want To Feel

Good Habits

My Inspiration

Self Care

Daily Task

☆_____
☆_____
☆_____
☆_____
☆_____

Today I am Grateful For _____

_____

The Moment I Loved Was _____

Good Ideas

Notes

Anxiety Journal

Date: Sun   Mon   Tue   Wed   Thu   Fri   Sat

Goals for Today

Energy Level: ☆ ☆ ☆ ☆ ☆

Activity Level: ☆ ☆ ☆ ☆ ☆

Sleep Quality: ☆ ☆ ☆ ☆ ☆

Mood

◇ Happy   ◇ Stressed

◇ Hopeful   ◇ Sad

◇ Calm   ◇ _____

◇ Tired   ◇ _____

Stressed About

▪ Triggers ▪

Symptoms

Coping Skills

Notes

Mindfulness Journal

Date:......./........./............   Sun Mon Tue Wed Thu Fri Sat

Todays Focus

I Want To Feel

Good Habits

My Inspiration

Self Care

Daily Task

☆ _____
☆ _____
☆ _____
☆ _____
☆ _____

Today I am Grateful For _____

The Moment I Loved Was _____

Good Ideas

Notes

Made in United States
Orlando, FL
13 February 2024